ONE PINK PIG
A Counting Book

For Zöe and Cleo

ONE PINK PIG
A Counting Book

Written and illustrated by
Sandy Nightingale
Andersen Press · London

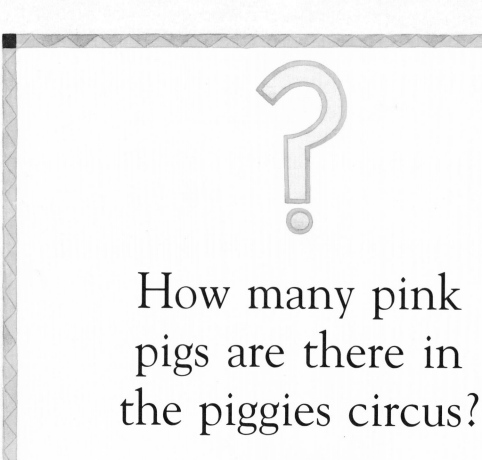

How many pink
pigs are there in
the piggies circus?

One pink pig
peeling potatoes.

Two pink pigs
painting pictures.

Three pink pigs
practising
pirouettes.

Four pink pigs on
a prancing
pantomime pony.

Five pink pigs
playing pirates.

Six pink pigs on
pogo sticks.

Seven pink pigs
throwing pies at a
picnic party.

Eight pink pigs
are pilots in
planes.

Nine pink pigs
pillow fighting in
their pyjamas.

Ten pink pigs
performing a
piggy pyramid.

Oops! Perhaps
they need more
practice.